The Selma Erving Collection
Modern Illustrated Books

Published by the Smith College Museum of Art, Northampton, Massachusetts, with funds provided in part by
the Museum Members.

Printed in the United States of America by The Meriden
Gravure Company. Photocomposition by Eastern Photo-
comp.

Cover: Henri Matisse, detail from p. 88 of Charles d'Orléans, *Poèmes*.

The Selma Erving Collection
Modern Illustrated Books

Introduction by Ruth Mortimer

CATALOGUE PREPARED BY COLLES BAXTER, CHARLES CHETHAM, BETSY JONES, JOHN LAN- CASTER, LINDA MUEHLIG, SARAH ULEN; EDITED BY JOHN LANCASTER

Smith College Museum of Art

Northampton, Massachusetts   1977

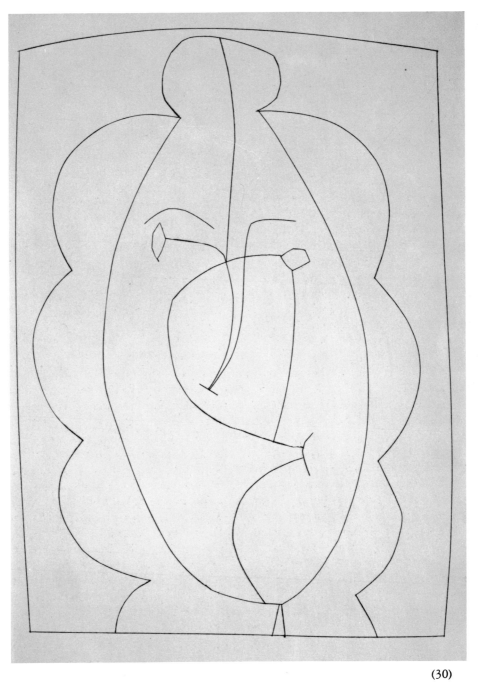

(30)

Foreword

The collection of modern illustrated books documented in this catalogue is one of two handsome donations Selma Erving ('27) made to the Smith College Museum of Art in 1972 and 1976. Five years ago Miss Erving presented the Museum with a collection of 144 late 19th and early 20th century prints and drawings. Last year, she made a second gift of 114 books and portfolios, including many valuable special reference works with which she had pursued the study of her own collection. Miss Erving has a passion for prints, drawings and illustrated books created at the turn of the century and later. Often the books she collected were planned and executed by artists whose prints she already owned. In some instances, she bought prints and drawings which figured as or are related to illustrations in her books. Her prints, books and drawings were valued not only for themselves but for their interrelationships: Miss Erving conceived of her collection as a coherent whole. When she made her gift of books, she asked that they be housed in the Museum's Print Room so that generations of Smith students and visitors might study them together with individual prints and drawings by the same artists.

In September of 1976, John Lancaster came to Northampton from Cambridge where he and his wife, Ruth Mortimer, the newly appointed Curator of Rare Books at Smith, had worked at the Houghton Library, Harvard. Having seen the Erving donation and realizing its quality, Mr. Lancaster volunteered to catalogue the books. Through the fall he verified and added to the information at hand. In the late fall, we decided to make his work the basis of a publication to which all members of the curatorial staff would add. The publication of the catalogue would coincide with an exhibition (May 7-October 9, 1977) celebrating the fiftieth anniversary of Miss Erving's graduation from Smith. In January of 1977 Colles Baxter, Assistant Curator of Prints, Sarah Ulen and Linda Muehlig, NEA Interns,

Betsy Jones, Associate Director of the Museum, and I began completing entries. In documenting the books and in the production of the catalogue we came to depend upon John Lancaster's professional skill and experience which have been crucial to the success of the enterprise. He is, in fact, editor of this catalogue.

In the fall of 1976, Ruth Mortimer, who contributed the introduction to this catalogue, gave a seminar entitled "The Composition of Books." Her students examined a number of books in the Erving collection and one session was held in the Print Room. A member of that seminar, Pamela Kinsey, of the class of 1977, turned her report into a note on the collection for the Spring issue of the *Alumnae Quarterly*. Miss Erving's gift has already occasioned friendly cooperation among many. Her books have drawn to the Museum and to the Rare Book Room many students to study and to enjoy great art of a kind never before seen at the College in such quality or depth.

The catalogue of the Erving Collection will be published in two volumes. The present volume, *The Selma Erving Collection: MODERN ILLUSTRATED BOOKS,* which appears now, will be followed in 1978 by *The Selma Erving Collection: PRINTS.* The projected second volume of the Erving Collection might have been the first. In 1972 when the first donation was made, Elizabeth Mongan, then Curator of Prints at the Museum, together with Marilyn Symmes, an assistant in the Print Room and now Assistant Curator of Graphic Arts at The Detroit Institute of Arts, began to catalogue the collection. When Miss Mongan retired in June of 1975, the catalogue was virtually completed, but until the appointment of Colles Baxter as Assistant Curator of Prints in December 1975, work came to a standstill. In April and May 1976 Miss Erving made her second large donation. Because it included 80 additional prints and 6 drawings, it was agreed that Miss Mongan's catalogue should include these new gifts. Miss Mongan had twice arranged impressive exhibitions of major parts of Miss Erving's gift, first in 1973 (May 8-May 27, and again September 11-October 28, 1973) and again in 1975 (April 24-June 1, 1975, continued to September 21, 1975) in an exhibition marking Miss Mongan's retirement. She has graciously agreed to write the introductory essay for the forthcoming catalogue of the prints.

We have received much considerate help in the preparation of the present volume. At the outset we turned to the standard catalogue, *The artist and the book* (Boston, 1961; revised edition, 1972) and to Eleanor M. Garvey, Curator of the Department of Printing and Graphic Arts, Harvard College Library, who prepared that catalogue. Miss Garvey allowed us the freedom of her reference shelves and of her own records. David Becker, her Assistant Curator, helped in several ways. Wolfgang Freitag, Senior Lecturer in Fine Arts and Librarian of the Fine Arts Library, Harvard College Library, allowed John Lancaster and me the use of the library. Margery Cohn, Conservator of Paper, Fogg Art Museum, gave us technical advice. Riva Castleman, Director, and Howardena Pindell, Assistant Curator of the Department of Prints and Illustrated Books, The Museum of Modern Art, shared information with Betsy Jones.

Greatest thanks are due to Selma Erving who, after all, or rather before all, formed the collection which has enriched this College and Museum and provided us with a focus for our energies.

CHARLES CHETHAM
Director

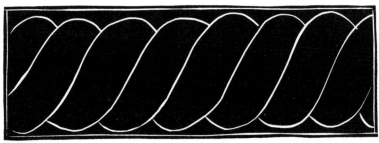

(22)

(22)

(23)

Introduction

In the year 1900, Ambroise Vollard published in Paris a book with the title *Parallèlement,* in which text by the poet Paul Verlaine was illustrated with lithographs by Pierre Bonnard. The project evolved through a series of chance encounters recalled by Vollard in an article, "Comment je devins éditeur," written in 1929.* Vollard was a picture dealer, prompted by the publisher's imprint "Ambroise Firmin-Didot, éditeur" to speculate on the attractions of "Ambroise Vollard, éditeur." He found first the type, Garamond, then the poet, Verlaine, then the artist, Bonnard; the sequence is worth remembering as Vollard remembered it, since the initial impulse was a desire to combine visual elements.

Parallèlement was a prophetic book, in design and execution of such quality that it was difficult for Vollard himself to match it in subsequent publications. It was the first true *livre de peintre* or *livre d'artiste*. By definition, the *livre d'artiste* must be illustrated with original graphic work, not reproductions, conceived and (usually) executed by an artist known primarily as a painter or sculptor, not a professional book illustrator. The negative parts of the definition point to the real distinction of these books, and the reason for their existence.

In the 1880s, photomechanical methods of reproduction and the proliferation of ordinary illustrators were reducing the book to a very minor art. Concern for the illustrated book was not confined to France, but by 1900 the extraordinary constellation of artists required to realize such a concept as the *livre d'artiste* was in Paris, accessible to Vollard and willing to experiment. For four decades, Vollard published books illustrated by such artists as Bonnard, Rodin, Denis, Dufy, Picasso, and Rouault. Other projects initiated by Vollard—the Braque Hesiod (7), the Chagall Gogol (10), the Segonzac Virgil (33)—were completed by other publishers who gradually entered the field. It was Vollard's idea to produce a book worthy of the art collector's serious attention.

The first French renaissance in the arts of the book occurred during the sixteenth century, when a few French printers and type designers rejected the gothic letter and heavily shaded woodcuts that threatened to remain the standard expressive vocabulary. It may not be a coincidence that three of the most exciting books of the twentieth century are editions of works of Pierre de Ronsard, as interpreted by Maillol (17), Matisse (24), and Segonzac (34). Ronsard was the major literary figure of the second half of the sixteenth century, when the French book had been revitalized by roman and italic types of genuine beauty and lasting influence and by woodcuts of elegance and delicate line. The Garamond type that first inspired Vollard is a sixteenth-century French font. The sixteenth-century spirit of innovation reappears: the *livre d'artiste* is seldom antiquarian. The "manuscript" books, such as Matisse's handsome Charles d'Orléans (25), are not a nostalgic return to the days before printing but a direct contact between artist and reader in a contemporary setting. Their manuscript antecedents are in William Blake, in the individual vision, not in the scriptorium or atelier. The artists of these books were preoccupied with transformations, and the book was thus transformed.

The collector needs to consider these books to see not only how the artist's hand works in an individual print but how his mind works on a sustained series of literary images. Comparisons can be made between two artists working on the same text, in cumulative effect somewhat different from examination of two paintings of the same subject. Why, for instance, did the French painters feel such an affinity with Virgil, Maillol working with the *Eclogues* (15) and the *Georgics* (20), Segonzac also with the *Georgics* (33), Villon with

*Reprinted in *Catalogue complet des éditions Ambroise Vollard* [exh. cat.], Paris, Le Portique [1930], pp. 5-19; first appeared in *Art vivant,* Dec. 15, 1929.

the *Bucolics* (35)? New translations of classical authors alternated with first printings of modern writers. Both figuratively and literally, author and artist were brought together in a personal confrontation from which the book emerged.

The choice of printing process for the illustrations fell naturally at first on lithography, the most recent in invention. The artist could draw directly on the stone. The resulting improvisational quality had advantages for the modern artist. Matisse sketched heads for Pierre Reverdy's *Visages* (23) larger than the page, breaking all rules for margins and conveying a sense of life beyond the dimensions of the book. The range of expression possible within a single process is perhaps best demonstrated by placing the open line of Matisse's *Visages* beside the black depths of tone explored by Redon in his series for Flaubert's *La tentation de Saint Antoine* (31).

The lithograph was the newest of the print media. The oldest, the woodcut, had less appeal for French artists, although Maillol successfully brought it into the modern book by following Italian models rather than French gothic. Matisse took another relief process, the linoleum block, and reversed the line to white on black.

The traditional harmony of the woodblock with type in a single printing process may have attracted Maillol as a sculptor in search of classic forms, but other artists preferred the subtleties of the intaglio plate. Many of the effects these twentieth-century artists wanted for their books could only be obtained by the etching process. Picasso used several etching techniques within a single book: in Césaire's *Corps perdu* (30), the poem titles are lift-ground and aquatint, the illustrations drypoint.

Historically we find the copperplate engraving gradually replacing the woodcut for book illustration in the late sixteenth century, the lithograph passing in and out of fashion in the nineteenth. In the twentieth-century book, the need to experiment with technique is so strong that all of the earlier methods are revived simultaneously and re-examined. Two different techniques may be employed in the same book. Rouault's *Cirque de l'étoile filante* (32) is richly illustrated with both wood-engravings and color etchings. The glowing circus colors would be too strong for the full program of illustration, while the wood-engravings alone would tell only half of Rouault's story.

The book form tempts the artistic imagination to respond in some surprising ways. When Bonnard illustrated Mirbeau's *Dingo* (4) with full-page etchings, he also designed illustrative headpieces, tailpieces, and initials as smaller etchings in the text. These smaller etchings supply a sort of running commentary on the text, different from his formal statement of subject matter in the plates. Chagall's plan of illustrations for Gogol's *Dead souls* (10) was similar, while Maillol, Matisse, and others designed purely decorative or calligraphic material to supplement more straightforward illustration and often continued this decorative invention in the cover or slipcase designs. Maillol supervised the papermaking for his books, producing paper of special composition and texture with his own watermark.

For the artists who became involved in these aspects of book production, the *livre d'artiste* was a challenge—an object of beauty put together out of disparate materials by the continual substitution of the unusual for the commonplace. The French *livres d'artistes* are printed with a *justification du tirage,* a statement of the number of copies printed according to a scheme that provides for special copies on finer paper, often with extra suites of the illustrations. Most of these books were printed in editions of two or three hundred copies, each copy numbered and signed by the artist. Frequently the *justification* carries the note that the lithographic stones or the etching plates were erased or the woodblocks destroyed after printing the stated number of copies. The suites of illustrations were sometimes printed in a different color or augmented to include additional designs prepared for the book by the artist but rejected in the final printing. The book as completed retains something of the creative process. To the author, the artist, and the publisher is added the collector, who opens the book with the pleasure of participation in that process.

RUTH MORTIMER
Curator of Rare Books

(5)

There have been two major exhibitions focussing on the *livre d'artiste.* The first was at the Museum of Modern Art in 1936, *Modern painters and sculptors as illustrators,* with a catalogue by Monroe Wheeler. The second, *The artist and the book 1860-1960,* at the Museum of Fine Arts, Boston, in 1961, was significantly broader in scope, as its title indicates. The Boston exhibition catalogue, compiled by Eleanor M. Garvey, with an introduction by Philip Hofer, has become an indispensable reference work for collectors and art historians.

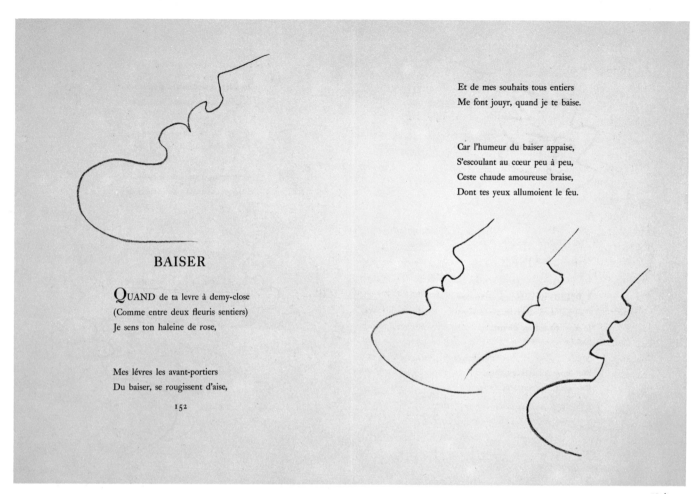

BAISER

QUAND de ta levre à demy-close
(Comme entre deux fleuris sentiers)
Je sens ton haleine de rose,

Mes lévres les avant-portiers
Du baiser, se rougissent d'aise,

152

Et de mes souhaits tous entiers
Me font jouyr, quand je te baise.

Car l'humeur du baiser appaise,
S'escoulant au cœur peu à peu,
Ceste chaude amoureuse braise,
Dont tes yeux allumoient le feu.

(24)

The Selma Erving collection, consisting of 110 books
and 4 portfolios of prints related to books, is presented
in this publication in the following order:
    Livres d'artistes
    Books containing original prints
    Portfolios containing prints related to specific books
    Books illustrated with reproductions
    Reference books
The *Livres d'artistes* are fully catalogued here. All other
titles are listed according to the cited categories. The
prints in portfolios will be fully documented in the
publication *PRINTS: The Selma Erving Collection.*

Livres d'artistes

Leonard Baskin   1922-

(1)

VOYAGES; SIX POEMS

Hart Crane

New York, The Museum of Modern Art, 1957

11f. incl. 3 wood-engravings printed in black (unsigned); 3 wood-engravings on tissue *hors texte,* one, pasted across a centerfold, printed in black, one in orange and one in 2 shades of green printed on recto and (rotated 90°) on verso (all unsigned); one woodcut *hors texte* printed in black on green Moriki (unsigned); press device printed in red; page size $9^1/_2 \times 11$ inches (245×280mm).

Printer: Leonard Baskin at The Gehenna Press (Harold P. McGrath, pressman)

Copy no. 326 of an edition of 1000 copies, incl. 25 *hors commerce.* Signed in ink below the colophon: Leonard Baskin.

1976: 18-86

Artist and the Book, 13

(2)

Emile Bernard   1868-1941

(2)

OEUVRES

François Villon

Paris, Ambroise Vollard (1918)

4f., 432p., 5f. incl. 312 full-page, half-page and vignette woodcuts (some repeated) printed in black or red-brown (all unsigned); page size $12^3/_4 \times 10$ inches (325×255 mm).

Printer: Emile Fequet under the supervision of the artist.

One of 225 copies on wove paper watermarked François Villon. Edition: 254 copies (2 on satin; 2 on holland colored by the artist, one in gouache; 25 on Shizuoka japan; 225 on wove). Copy no. 231.

1976: 18-87

Note: 20 suites of the woodcuts on wove were separately issued. This copy contains 4 additional loose full-page woodcuts.

(1)

(3)

(4)

DINGO

Octave Mirbeau

Paris, Ambroise Vollard, 1924

193, [1]p., 2f. incl. 40 etchings printed in black (12 signed with monogram PB on the plate), of which 13 are illustrated initial letters; 14 etchings *hors texte* printed in black (12 signed with monogram PB on the plate); wood-engraved table of etchings included in

Pierre Bonnard   1867-1947

(3)

PETITES SCÈNES FAMILIÈRES POUR PIANO

Claude Terrasse, composer; lyrics by Franc-Nohain

Paris, E. Fromont [ca. 1893]

2f., 36p., 1f., 37-61, [1]p. incl. 19 lithographs printed in black (17 signed with monogram PB on the stone); lithographed cover printed in black; page size $13^3/_4 \times 10^3/_4$ inches (350×275 mm).

Printer: Crevel Frères

1976:18-90

Artist and the Book, 25

(4)

collation; additional etching on cover printed in black (unsigned); page size 15 × 11 inches (380 × 280 mm).

Printer: Louis Fort, etchings
        Emile Fequet, text

One of 280 copies on Arches laid. Edition: 370 copies (30 on old japan, 40 on Shizuoka japan, 280 on Arches laid, 20 *hors commerce* on Arches laid). Copy no. 336.

1976:18-89

Artist and the Book, 30

(5)

SAINTE MONIQUE

Ambroise Vollard

Paris, Ambroise Vollard, 1930

2f., ix, [1], 222p., 4f. incl. 140 wood-engravings printed in black (unsigned); 37 wood-engravings ("bois non utilisées") *hors texte* printed in black (unsigned); 17 etchings *hors texte* (of which 3 are the table of *hors texte* illustrations) printed in black (14 signed with monogram PB on the plate); 29 lithographs *hors texte* printed in black (all signed with monogram PB on the stone); additional wood-engraving on cover printed in black (unsigned); page size 13 × 10 inches (330 × 255 mm).

Printer: Aimé Jourde, text

One of 257 copies on Arches wove. Edition: 390 copies (8 on old japan, 25 on imperial japan, and 50 on Arches linen, all with a suite of the etchings and lithographs; 257 on Arches wove; 35 *hors commerce;* 15 for exhibition). Copy no. 191.

1976:18-93

(5)

Georges Braque   1882-1963

(6)

UNE AVENTURE MÉTHODIQUE

Pierre Reverdy

(Paris) Fernand Mourlot, 1949 (1950)

60p., 27f. incl. 26 lithograph vignettes printed in black and frontispiece printed in 3 colors with yellow and red added by hand (unsigned); additional lithograph on cover in blue (unsigned); 12 reproductions of paintings in color (the first and the last of the reproductions unnumbered, the remaining ten numbered I-X); page size 17³/₈ × 13 inches (440 × 330 mm).

Printer: J. Dumoulin, text (H. Barthélemy, supervisor)

Mourlot Frères, lithographs and reproductions

Publishers: Fernand Mourlot and André Sauret

Copy no. 95 of an edition of 265 copies on Arches wove incl. 15 *hors commerce,* signed in pencil: Georges Braque [and] Pierre Reverdy.

1976:18-95

(7)

THÉOGONIE *(Text in Greek)*

Hesiod

(Paris) Maeght, 1955

77, [1]p., 2f. incl. 18 mixed etchings printed in black (16 blind stamped with monogram GB in a circle on page margin); frontispiece in etching and aquatint printed in black and tan; etched cover in black varnished in yellow by the artist; photo-engraved table of illustrations; page size 17¹/₄ × 12³/₄ inches (440 × 325 mm).

Printer: Fequet et Baudier

Copy no. 68 of an edition of 150 copies on Auvergne signed in pencil below colophon: G Braque.

1972:50-6

Artist and the Book, 38

Note: 16 etchings were made by Braque in 1932 from drawings made in the previous year. 50 suites of these on holland

with remarques were issued by Vollard in 1932 without texts; in these, 10 etchings were signed by the artist in pencil or brown crayon, 6 were left unsigned; there were also 50 suites of plates I-IV in the first state, and a number of trial proofs in various states, incl. 3 for the frontispiece printed in black and tan.

Massimo Campigli 1895-1971

(8)

LIRICHE

Sappho; trans. Manar Valgimigli

Venice, Edizioni del Cavallino (1944)

30f.; 12 lithographs *hors texte* printed in black (signed and dated campigli 44 on the stone); Officina Bodoni device printed in red; page size 15¹/₂ × 11¹/₄ inches (395 × 285 mm).

Printer: Stamperia del Cavallino, lithographs Officina Bodoni (Giovanni Mardersteig, director), text

One of 110 copies on Marais without suite. Edition: 125 copies (3 on Madagascar with suite on japan; 12 on Marais with suite on japan; 110 on Marais without suite). Copy no. 101.

1976:18-97

(8)

(6)

(7)

Marc Chagall   1887-

(9)

MATERNITÉ

Marcel Arland

Paris, Au Sans Pareil, 1926

2f., 95p., 1f.; 5 etchings *hors texte* printed in black (unsigned); page size $8^1/_8 \times 6^1/_4$ inches (205×160 mm).

Printer: Louis Fort, etchings
        R. Coulouma, text

One of 765 copies on Lafuma de Voiron. Edition: 960 copies (20 on laid with 2 suites, reserved for the Amis du Sans Pareil; 35 on japan with 2 suites; 60 on holland laid with one suite; 80 on holland laid; 765 on Lafuma de Voiron wove). There were also some un-numbered copies *hors commerce*. Copy no. 507.

1976:18-99

Note: Kornfeld mentions a new edition, no date given, printed by Paul Haasen, possibly of the etchings only, consisting of 6 copies for the Archiv Saint-Paul-de-Vence, of which 5 are on VM laid and one is on japan.

(10)

LES ÂMES MORTES

Nikolai Gogol; trans. Henri Mongault

Paris, Tériade, 1948

2 volumes; 108 mixed etchings and 11 etched initial letters; page size 15×11 inches (380×280 mm).
I: 2f., 160p., 1f. incl. 6 headpieces and 6 initial letters printed in black (unsigned); 51 mixed etchings *hors texte* printed in black (36 signed on the plate Chagall, M. Chagall, or Marc Chagall).
II: 3f., 165-308p., 16f. incl. 5 headpieces and 5 initial letters printed in black (unsigned); 46 mixed etchings *hors texte* (41 signed on the plate Chagall or **M**. Chagall); 11f. illustrated table of etchings included in the collation.

Printer: Louis Fort, *hors texte* etchings (1927)
        Raymond Haasen, text etchings (1948)
        L'Imprimerie Nationale (Raymond Blanchet, director; composition and printing under the direction of Georges Arnoult), text

One of 285 copies without suite. Edition: 368 signed copies on Arches wove watermarked LES ÂMES MORTES (50 with a suite on japan *nacré*; 285 without suite; 33 *hors commerce*). Copy no. 67. This copy signed in ink on preliminary leaf: Marc Chagall.

1976:18-100

Artist and the Book, 50

(9)

(10)

Note: Ambroise Vollard commissioned the illustrations in 1923. 100 hors texte plates, an illustrated table of plates, and a set of headpieces were executed between 1923 and 1927, and printed in 1927. The book remained unpublished at Vollard's death in 1938. In 1948 Tériade issued the book, using 96 of the original etchings (one printed twice, as the frontispiece and plate XX in v. 1), with initial letters and new headpieces executed in 1947, the original headpieces having been lost.

Jean Charlot   1898-

(11)

PICTURE BOOK

Jean Charlot; inscriptions by Paul Claudel; trans. Elise Cavanna

New York, John Becker, 1933

69f. incl. 32 lithographs printed in color (all signed on the plate Jean Charlot; some also dated 33) and

(10)

lithographed vignette on title-page (signed J. C. on the plate); title-page vignette reproduced in black on cover; additional lithograph printed in rust on tan wrapper; page size 11 × 8¹/₂ inches (280 × 215 mm).

Printer: Will A. Kistler Company (Lynton R. Kistler, hand typesetter; Edward Broughton, off-set pressman)

Designer: Merle Armitage

Copy no. 287 of an edition of 500 (32 specially anno-tated artist's copies with signed original sketch and set of progressive proofs of one of the plates; 468 regular issue without sketch and extra proofs). This copy signed in ink on colophon page: Jean Charlot, Lynton R. Kistler, Merle Armitage.

1976:18-101

Artist and the Book, 54

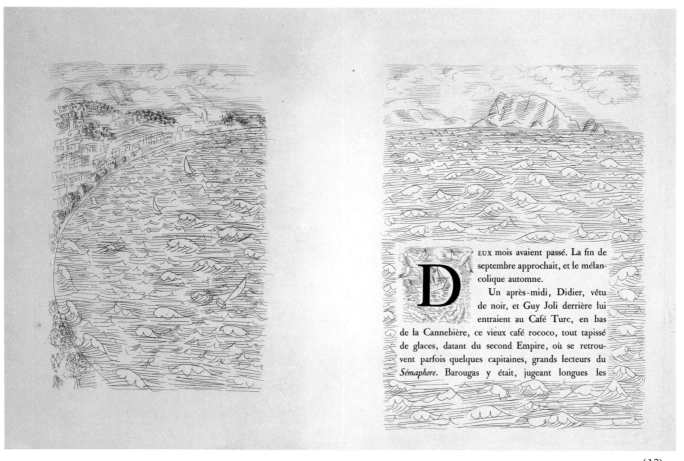

EUX mois avaient passé. La fin de septembre approchait, et le mélancolique automne.

Un après-midi, Didier, vêtu de noir, et Guy Joli derrière lui entraient au Café Turc, en bas de la Cannebière, ce vieux café rococo, tout tapissé de glaces, datant du second Empire, où se retrouvent parfois quelques capitaines, grands lecteurs du *Sémaphore.* Barougas y était, jugeant longues les

(12)

Raoul Dufy   1877-1953

(12)

LA BELLE-ENFANT, OU L'AMOUR À QUARANTE ANS

Eugène Montfort

Paris, Ambroise Vollard, 1930

2f., 249, [1]p., 4f. incl. 77 etchings printed in black (unsigned); 16 etchings *hors texte* printed in black (unsigned); illustrated table of etchings included in collation; etched cover; page size 13 × 10 inches (325 × 250 mm).

Printer: Louis Fort, etchings
           L'Imprimerie Nationale (Gilbert Peycelon, director), text

One of 245 copies on Arches wove. Edition: 390 copies (30 on old japan with a suite on Montval laid; 35 on japan *supernacré* with a suite on Montval laid; 35 on japan *supernacré* without suite; 245 on Arches wove; 35 *hors commerce;* 15 for exhibition). Copy no. 311.

1976:18-103

Artist and the Book, 93

(13)

Hans Erni   1909-

(13)

FABLES

Jean de La Fontaine

Lausanne, André Gonin (1955)

53, [1]p. incl. 35 lithographs printed in black (the frontispiece signed with monogram e and dated 1.16.55 in reverse on the stone, the rest unsigned); 30 lithographs *hors texte* printed in black, being illustrations not used in the work (unsigned); additional lithograph printed in black on a colored ground across covers; page size 13³/₄ × 10 inches (350 × 255 mm).

Printer: Hermann Kratz (with Emile Matthieu),
         lithographs
         André Kundig (with Auguste Griess), text

One of 294 ordinary copies. Edition: 345 copies on Rives (1 with original drawings and a suite on china; 10 with a suite on china and a single drawing each; 15 with a suite on china; 294 ordinary copies; 25 *hors commerce*). Copy no. 203. Signed on p. 9: André Gonin [and] H. Erni.

1976:18-104

Jean Louis Forain   1852-1911

(14)

CROQUIS PARISIENS

Joris Karl Huysmans

Paris, Henri Vaton, 1880

108p., 1f. incl. etched frontispiece printed in black (signed j. l. forain on the plate); 3 etchings *hors texte* by Forain printed in black (1 signed j. l. forain on the plate, 1 signed forain on the plate); 4 etchings *hors texte* by Raffaëlli printed in black (signed J. F. RAFFAËLLI on the plate, one dated 79); page size 8³/₄ × 6 inches (215 × 150 mm).

Printer: Félix Callewoert père

One of 500 unnumbered copies on holland. Edition: 545 copies (5 on china with double set of etchings; 20 on japan; 20 on Whatman; 500 on holland).

1976:18-106

Artist and the Book, 108

Note: This copy lacks one of the etchings by Raffaëlli.

(14: FORAIN)

(15)

Printer: Cranach Presse (Count Harry Kessler and J. H.
    Mason in charge; Walter Tanz, com-
    positor; Erich Dressler, H. Gage-Cole,
    and Max Kopp, pressmen; Erich Hillhof,
    assistant)

One of 250 copies on handmade rag. Edition: 294
copies (8 on vellum, incl. 3 *hors commerce;* 36 on
Kessler-Maillol silk rag, incl. 10 *hors commerce;* 250 on
handmade rag, incl. 25 *hors commerce,* with a watermark representing Maillol's statue *La Méditerranée*
with Maillol's and Kessler's initials on the base). Copy
no. 28.

1976:18-117

Artist and the Book, 172

*Note: The printing of the Latin-German edition was begun
in 1914, interrupted by the war, and resumed in 1925.
There were also Latin-French and Latin-English editions.*

(16)

L'ART D'AIMER

Ovid; trans. Henri Borneque

(Lausanne, Les Frères Gonin) 1935

122p., 1f. incl. 12 lithographs, 7 printed in black
and 5 in sanguine (signed M in a circle on the stone)
and 15 woodcuts, incl. 4 illustrated initial letters,
printed in black (unsigned); additional woodcut on
cover; page size $15^{1}/_{8} \times 11$ inches (385×280 mm).

Printer: Edmond Desjobert, lithographs
    Philippe Gonin, woodcuts and text

Unnumbered, unsigned copy, not included in the justification, designated in letterpress: *Exemplaire d'artiste.* Edition: 275 copies on Maillol's special Canson
and Montgolfier paper, watermarked with the statue
La Méditerranée with the names Maillol and Gonin on
the base (225 copies for Gonin, incl. 125 *hors commerce;*
50 for A. Zwemmer of London, incl. 25 *hors commerce*).

1976:18-112

Artist and the Book, 173

Aristide Maillol   1861-1944

(15)

ECLOGAE & GEORGICA: ECLOGAE (*Text in Latin and
    German*)

Virgil; trans. Rudolf Alexander Schröder

(Weimar, Cranach Presse; Leipzig, Inselverlag; 1926)

2f., 110p., 3f. incl. 43 woodcuts by Maillol printed
in black (1 signed AM on the block); xylographic
title, initial letters, and press mark letters designed
and cut by Eric Gill, the ornament of these letters designed by Maillol and cut by Gill; page size 13×10
inches (325×250 mm).

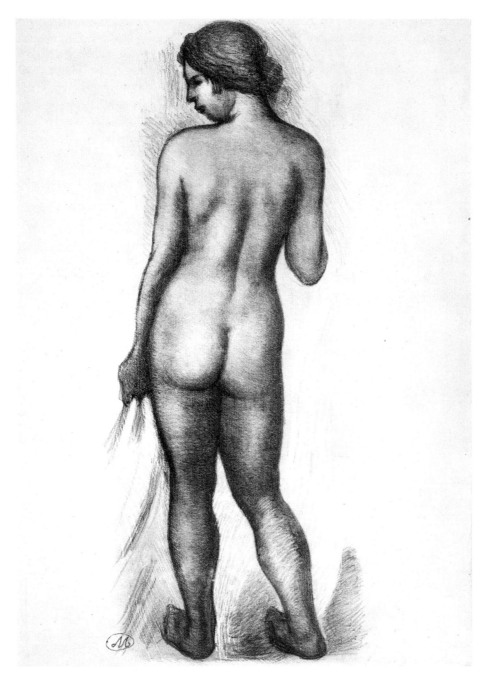

(16)

Note: Gonin had Maillol's drawings copied in lithography by an unnamed person; Maillol was dissatisfied with the results but "corrected" the prints in a single day. (See Günter Busch, Aristide Maillol als Illustrator, *Neu-Isenberg, 1970, p. [14].)*

   A supplementary edition of 50 proofs of each of the full-page lithographs in sanguine on Montval was produced with Maillol's agreement.

(17)

LIVRET DE FOLASTRIES

Pierre de Ronsard

Paris, Ambroise Vollard, 1938 (1940)

190p., 4f. incl. 25 etchings printed in black (unsigned); 16 etchings *hors texte* printed in black (unsigned); 2 additional etchings printed in black on covers (unsigned); 16 wood-engravings, constituting the *Table des hors texte,* printed in black (unsigned); page size 9³/₈ × 7³/₈ inches (240 × 185 mm).

(17)

Printer: Roger Lacourière, etchings
        Henri Jourde, wood-engravings
        Lucien Vollard and Martin Fabiani on the
           presses of Henri Jourde, text
Blockcutter: Georges Aubert

One of 25 *hors commerce* copies on Montval laid. Edition: 260 copies (30 on imperial japan (signed), plus 5 *hors commerce;* 200 on Montval laid (unsigned), plus 25 *hors commerce*). Copy no. XII.

1976:18-114

(18)

CONCERT D'ÉTÉ

Joseph-Sébastien Pons

Paris, Flammarion (1945)

1f., 148p., 2f. incl. 26 woodcuts printed in black (unsigned); page size 11¹/₄ × 8³/₄ inches (285 × 220 mm).

Printer: Pierre Bouchet

One of 200 copies on Lana without suite. Edition: 315 copies (10 on japan with a suite on china; 20 on Lana with a suite on japan; 20 on Lana with a suite on Lana; 200 on Lana without suite; 5 on japan and 10 on Lana for the collaborators; 50 on Lana for the artist). Copy no. 169.

1976:18-113

(19)

DIALOGUES DES COURTISANES

Lucian; trans. Charles Astruc

Paris, Fernand Mourlot, 1948

2f., 93, [1]p., 2f. incl. 35 lithographs (incl. frontispiece) printed in black (unsigned); page size 15 × 11³/₈ inches (380 × 285 mm).

Printer: Fernand Mourlot, lithographs
        Pierre Bricage, text

(18)

Copy no. 248 of an edition of 275 copies on Maillol's special Canson and Montgolfier paper watermarked with VM monogram in a circle with FRANCE beneath (50 with a suite in sanguine; 15 *hors commerce*).

1976:18-111

Note: The lithographs for this book, although not executed by the artist, were done from his original drawings under his guidance. See Busch, p. 12.

There were also 5 separate suites on various papers.

(20)

LES GÉORGIQUES (*Text in Latin and French*)

Virgil; trans. Jacques Delille

Paris, Philippe Gonin, 1937-1943 (1950)

2 volumes; 122 woodcuts incl. repetitions (of which some are illustrated initial letters); page size $12^5/_8 \times 9^3/_8$ inches (325×240 mm).
I: 1f., 174 p., 1f. incl. 61 woodcuts printed in black (unsigned).
II: 1f., 154p., 1f. incl. 61 woodcuts printed in black (unsigned).

Printer: Philippe Gonin

Copy no. 121 of an edition of 750 copies on rag wove with the same watermark as in the Ovid *L'art d'aimer*.

1976:18–118-119

Artist and the Book, 175

Note: This copy is accompanied by 2 separate suites of the woodcuts, in black and in sanguine, all stamped with M in a circle, and 10 proof sheets of early states printed in sanguine on china.

(19)

Q VID faciat lætas segetes; quo sidere terram
Vertere, Mæcenas, ulmisque adjungere vites
Conveniat; quæ cura boum, qui cultus habendo
Sit pecori; apibus quanta experientia parcis,
Hinc canere incipiam. Vos, ô clarissima mundi
Lumina, labentem cælo quæ ducitis annum;
Liber et alma Ceres, vestro si munere tellus
Chaoniam pingui glandem mutavit aristâ,
Poculaque inventis Acheloïa miscuit uvis;
Et vos, agrestum præsentia numina, Fauni,
Ferte simul, Faunique pedem Dryadesque puellæ:
Munera vestra cano. Tuque ô, cui prima frementem
Fudit equum magno tellus percussa tridenti,

33

Albert Marquet 1875-1947

(21)

IMAGES D'UNE PETITE VILLE ARABE

Marcelle Marty

(Paris) Manuel Bruker (1947)

2f., 9-94p., 2f. incl. 25 etchings printed in black (unsigned); additional etching on wrapper printed in black (signed Marquet on the plate); additional suite of 26 etchings printed in black laid in (the first signed Marquet in pencil l.r. and numbered 3/20 in pencil l.l.; page size 12⁷/₈ × 9³/₄ inches (320 × 250 mm).

Printer: Padovani, etchings
              Jourde et Allard, text

One of 20 copies with an additional suite on japan *nacré*. Edition: 225 copies on Arches wove (incl. 20 with suite and 25 for collaborators). Copy no. 3.

1976:18-121

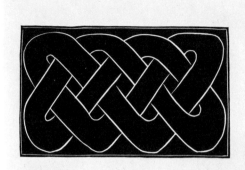

 E la tête au pied, comme l'arc, je tremble de l'envie de détruire.

     Moi, je suis malade de haine. O Dieu, ne me sera-t-il pas donné avant de mourir

     de voir peu à peu sous mon bras, toujours plus loin, tout alentour,

21

(22)

(21)

Henri Matisse 1869-1954

(22)

PASIPHAÉ, CHANT DE MINOS

Henri de Montherlant

(Paris) Martin Fabiani (1944)

121, [1]p., 3f. incl. 50 linoleum engravings printed in black (incl. frontispiece), 84 linoleum-engraved initial letters and repeated headband printed in red (unsigned); linoleum-engraved cover printed in blue; page size 12³/₄ × 9⁷/₈ inches (325 × 250 mm).

Printer: Fequet et Baudier

One of 200 copies on Arches wove watermarked Arches and Martin Fabiani. Edition: 250 copies (30 on japan with extra set of 12 cuts on china; 200 on Arches wove; 20 *hors commerce* on Arches wove). Copy no. 116. This copy signed in ink on preliminary leaf: Henri Matisse.

1976:18-124

Artist and the Book, 198

(23)

(23)

VISAGES

Pierre Reverdy

(Paris) Les Editions du Chêne (1946)

3f., 95, [1]p., 3f. incl. 14 lithographs printed in brown, 14 initial letters printed in mauve, and 14 linoleum-engraved *culs-de-lampe* printed in black (unsigned); linoleum-engraved cover design printed in black; page size 12⁷/₈ × 10¹/₈ inches (325 × 255 mm).

Printers: Mourlot Frères, lithographs
Fequet et Baudier, text and linoleum engravings

One of 200 copies on Lana wove. Edition: 250 copies (30 on Montval wove; 200 on Lana wove; 20 *hors commerce* on Lana wove). Copy no. 204. This copy signed in pencil on preliminary leaf: Henri Matisse [and] Pierre Reverdy.

1976:18-126

(24)

FLORILÈGE DES AMOURS

Pierre de Ronsard

Paris, Albert Skira (1948)

3f., [11]-185, [1]p., 2f. incl. 125 lithographs printed in brown and lithograph title vignette printed in black (all unsigned); 2 lithographs on cover printed in brown (unsigned); page size 15 × 11¹/₈ inches (380 × 280 mm).

Printer: Mourlot Frères, lithographs
Georges Girard, text

One of 250 ordinary copies. Edition: 320 copies on Arches wove (20 with a suite of 12 lithographs on imperial japan, numbered and monogrammed by the artist; 30 with a suite of 8 on imperial japan; 250 without suite; 20 *hors commerce*). Copy no. 62. This copy signed in black ink: H. Matisse [and in blue ink] Albert Skira.

1976:18-127

Artist and the Book, 201

(25)

POÈMES

Charles d'Orléans

(Paris) Tériade (1950)

100p., 2f. incl. 54 lithographs printed in color (the frontispiece signed and dated Henri Matisse 3/43 on the stone); lithographed text in artist's hand printed in black within lithographed borders in color; lithographed covers printed in color; page size 16 × 10³/₈ inches (405 × 265 mm).

Printer: Mourlot Frères

Copy no. 969 of an edition of 1230 signed copies on Arches, incl. 30 *hors commerce*. This copy signed in pencil below colophon: H. Matisse

1976:18-125

Artist and the Book, 202

(23)

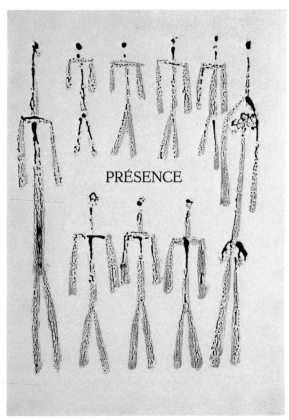

PRÉSENCE

(29)

1f., 96p., 2f.; frontispiece (combined etching-aquatint) *hors texte* printed in black (signed on the plate and in pencil at l.r.: pascin); page size 8 × 6 inches (205 × 150 mm).

Printer: La Roseraie, etching
       A. Lahure, text

One of 25 *hors commerce* copies, unnumbered. Edition: 350 copies (25 on imperial japan, 300 on Montval laid, 25 *hors commerce* on Montval laid). Inscribed on half-title: A Vincent [illegible] son ami André Salmon 1927.

1976:18-129

(26)

Jules Pascin   1885-1930

(26)

VÉNUS DANS LA BALANCE, POÈMES

André Salmon

Paris, Éditions des Quatre Chemins (1926)

Pablo Picasso   1881-1973

(27)

LYSISTRATA

Aristophanes; trans. Gilbert Seldes

New York, The Limited Editions Club, 1934

117, [1]p. incl. 6 etchings printed in black (1 signed and dated Picasso 4 Fevrier XXXIV in reverse on the plate) and 29 lithographs printed in sanguine (1 dated Paris 26 Decembre XXXIII on the stone) after 40 pencil drawings (some combined on one stone); page size 11¹/₂ × 9¹/₄ inches (290 × 235 mm).

Printer: The Printing Office of The Limited Editions
        Club (Julian E. Berla, manager; John F.
        McNamara, pressman; John T. Logan,
        lithographs)
Designer: George Macy

Copy no. 348 of an edition of 1500 copies on Rives. This copy signed in pencil below colophon: Picasso.

1976:18-135

Artist and the Book, 226

(28)

DOS CONTES: EL CENTAURE PICADOR, EL CAPVESPRE
    D'UN FAUNE

Ramon Reventos

Paris-Barcelona, Editorial Albor, 1947

28f. incl. 4 etchings printed in black (unsigned; 2 dated 5.2.47., 1 dated 4.2.47., 1 dated 6.2.47 in reverse on the plate); half-title, title page, divisional titles, and initial capitals reproduced in facsimile from artist's handwritten original; page size 13 × 10¹/₈ inches (330 × 260 mm).

Printer: Roger Lacourière, etchings
     R. Coulouma, text (Henri Jonquières,
     director)

One of 230 regular copies. Edition: 250 copies (20 with suite; 230 regular issue without suite). Copy no. 244.

1976:18-134

Artist and the Book, 232

(27)

(28)

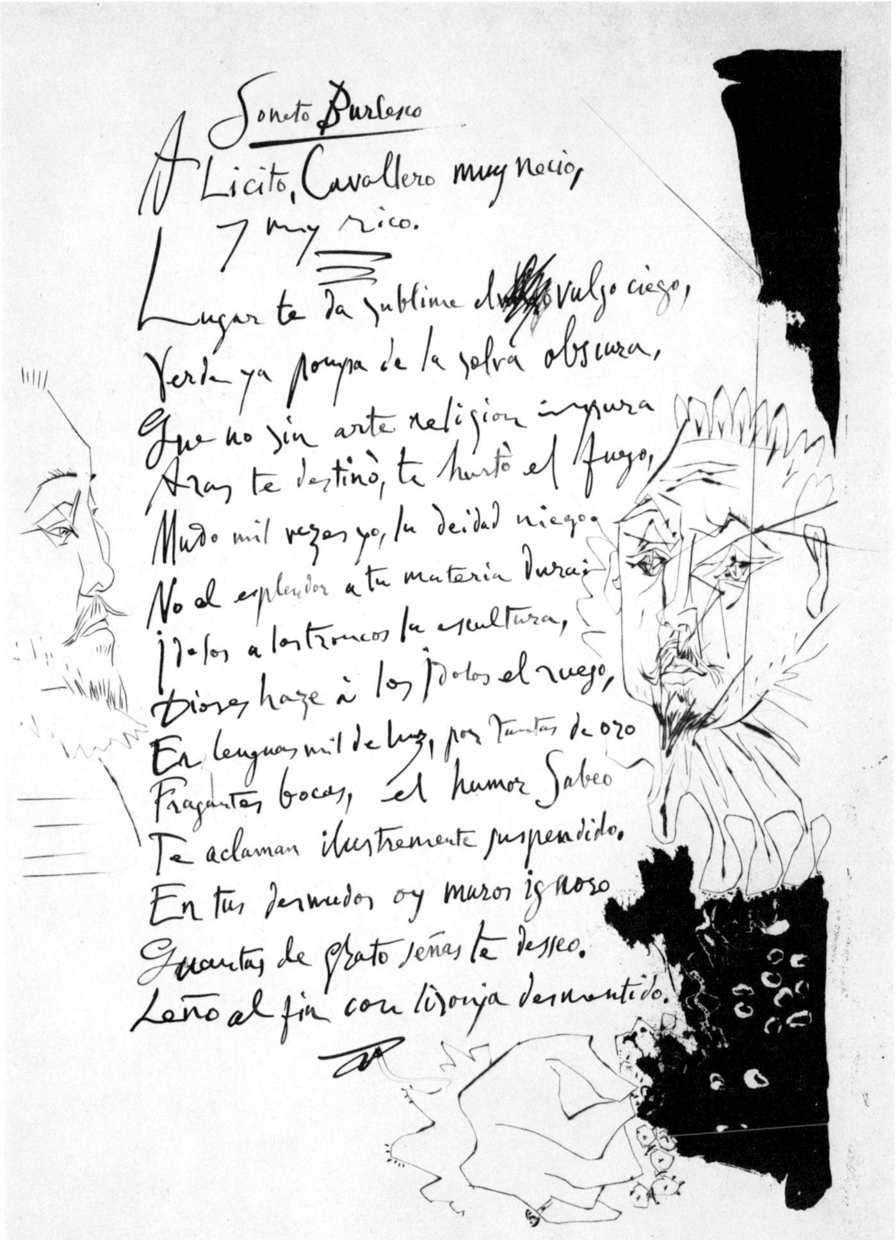

Soneto Burlesco

A Licio, Cavallero muy necio,
y muy rico.

Lugar te da sublime el vulgo ciego,
Verde ya pompa de la selva obscura,
Que no sin arte religión impura
Aras te destinó, te hurtó el fuego,

Mudo mil veces yo, la deidad niego
No el esplendor a tu materia dura;
Ídolos a los troncos la escultura,
Dioses haze á los ídolos el ruego,

En lenguas mil de luz, por tantas de oro
Fragantes bocas, el humor Sabeo
Te aclaman ilustremente suspendido.

En tus desnudos oy muros ignoro
Quantas de grato señas te desseo.
Leño al fin con lisonja desmentido.

(29)

(29)

VINGT POÈMES (*Text in French and Spanish*)

Gongora; trans. Z. Milner

(Paris, 1948)

85f. incl. 41 etchings with aquatint accents printed in black (unsigned), of which 20 are texts of the poems in Spanish; page size 15 × 11 inches (380 × 280 mm).

Printer: Roger Lacourière, etchings
       Fequet et Baudier, text

One of 235 copies on Marais watermarked Gongora. Edition: 275 copies (5 on imperial japan with a suite of all etchings on china and a suite of the first states of the 20 text plates; 10 on Marais with both suites; 235 on Marais without suite; 25 *hors commerce,* of which 5 have the suite of 20 text plates). Copy no. 232.

1976:18-131

(30)

CORPS PERDU

Aimé Césaire

Paris, Éditions Fragrance (1950)

4f., 123p., 2f. incl. 30 etchings (10 lift ground and aquatint with letterpress poem titles, 20 drypoint) printed in black (unsigned); drypoint frontispiece printed in black (unsigned); drypoint title on cover; page size 15³/₈ × 11¹/₄ inches (390 × 285 mm).

Printer: Roger Lacourière, etchings
      Pierre Bouchet, text

One of 200 copies on Montval wove watermarked *Corps perdu* after the artist's cover title. Edition: 219 signed copies (4 on japan *nacré* with suite on china; 3 on imperial japan with suite on china; 200 on Montval wove watermarked *Corps perdu,* incl. 23 with suite on old japan; 12 *hors commerce*). Copy no. 204. This copy signed in pencil on preliminary leaf: Picasso [and] A. Césaire.

1976:18-130

Artist and the Book, 233

Odilon Redon   1840-1916

(31)

LA TENTATION DE SAINT ANTOINE

Gustave Flaubert

(Paris) Ambroise Vollard, 1933 (1938)

2f., 205, [1]p., 1f. incl. 15 wood-engravings printed in black (all signed with monogram Od.R. on the block); 22 lithographs *hors texte* printed in black (unsigned); 22 wood-engravings *hors texte* printed in black

(30)

(31)

(32)

(unsigned), being the table of lithographs; 1 wood-engraving repeated on cover in black; page size 17¹/₂ × 13 inches (445 × 330 mm).

Printer: August Clot, lithographs
         Henri Jourde, text
Blockcutter: Georges Aubert

One of 185 copies on Arches wove. Edition: 220 copies (25 on Marais wove, 185 on Arches wove, 10 *hors commerce* on Arches wove). Copy no. 191.

1976:18-137

Note: an edition of the lithographs on china was published by Vollard in 1896 (including 2 lithographs not present here); these lithographs (on holland) were printed at that time and held aside for eventual book publication.

Georges Rouault   1871-1958

(32)

CIRQUE DE L'ÉTOILE FILANTE

Georges Rouault

Paris, Ambroise Vollard, 1938

2f., 168p., 3f. incl. 82 wood-engravings printed in black (signed G. Rouault or G.R., some dated from 1930 to 1934, on the block); 17 aquatints *hors texte* printed in color (all but one signed GR or G. Rouault and dated 1934 or 1935 on the plate); wood-engraved table of illustrations included in the collation; artist's device on cover; page size 17¹/₄ × 13¹/₄ inches (445 × 340 mm).

Printer: Roger Lacourière, aquatints
        "Aux Deux Ours" (Henri Jourde, pressman),
           wood-engravings and text
Blockcutter: Georges Aubert

One of 25 *hors commerce* copies on Montval laid. Edition: 280 copies (35 on imperial japan with a suite of the aquatints printed in black; 215 on Montval laid; 30 *hors commerce* incl. 5 on imperial japan and 25 on Montval laid). Copy no. XXVI.

1976:18-138

Artist and the Book, 271

Note: Around 1930 Vollard commissioned Rouault to illustrate a text by André Suarès entitled Cirque, *and he made 8 aquatints and 20 wood-engravings for it. While the printing was in process Vollard suspended publication, fearing the Suarès text might offend his American patrons. In 1932 Suarès agreed to Rouault's publishing the prints with Rouault's own text. Of the original illustrations,* Cirque de l'étoile filante *contains only the 20 wood-engravings; the aquatints and 62 additional wood-engravings are new.*

(32)

(34)

André Dunoyer de Segonzac
1884-1974

(33)

GEORGICA (*Text in Latin and French*)

Virgil; trans. Michel de Marolles

Paris, 1944 (1947)

2 volumes; 119 etchings with drypoint and aquatint accents; page size 18 × 13½ inches (455 × 345 mm). I: 201, [1]p., 1f. incl. 58 etchings printed in black (unsigned).

II: 213, [1]p., 4f. incl. 61 etchings printed in black (unsigned).

Printer: Jacques Frélaut, etchings (on the presses of Roger Lacourière)
L'Imprimerie Nationale, text

Copy no. 143 of an edition of 250 copies on Arches wove watermarked with spear of wheat and bee, incl. 50 with extra set of etchings on Rives wove and 25 *hors commerce.*

1976:18-140

Artist and the Book, 281

(34)

QUELQUES SONNETS

Pierre de Ronsard

(Paris, 1955)

103f. incl. 51 etchings printed in black (unsigned);
page size 12½ × 10 inches (315 × 255 mm).

Printer: Jacques Frélaut, etchings
        L'Imprimerie Nationale, text

One of 120 ordinary copies. Edition: 210 copies on
Arches wove (35 with a suite on japan, and an additional suite on holland of etchings not used in the
book; 40 with a suite on japan; 120 without suite; 15
author's copies). Copy no. 77.

1976:18-139

Jacques Villon   1875-1963

(35)

LES BUCOLIQUES (*Text in Latin and French*)

Virgil; trans. and with an essay by Paul Valéry

Paris, Scripta & Picta, 1953

xxx, [1], 126p., 5f. incl. 44 lithographs in color and
one in black (unsigned); page size 15 × 11¼ inches
(380 × 285 mm).

Printer: Célestin (Mourlot Frères), lithographs
        Frazier-Soye, text

This copy printed for Dr. A. Roudinesco, the dedi-
catee and president of Scripta & Picta. Edition: 269
copies (245 on Arches wove; 24 on japan *nacré* with a
suite in black and in color for the founding members
of Scripta & Picta). There were also several unnumbered *exemplaires nominatifs* for the collaborators.
Signed and dated in ink: Jacques Villon 1960.

1976:18-143

Note: There were also 35 suites in color on Arches wove.
   This copy specially bound by Henningsen in full red
morocco gilt-stamped with a geometric pattern.

Maurice de Vlaminck
1876-1958

(36)

LE DIABLE AU CORPS

Raymond Radiguet

Paris, Marcel Seheur (1926)

114p., 1f. incl. 10 lithographs printed in black, 1
lithograph initial letter and 1 lithograph *cul-de-lampe*
printed in brown (all unsigned); 1 drypoint etching
hors texte printed in black (unsigned); page size
11½ × 9¾ inches (290 × 245 mm).

Printer: Marcel Seheur

One of 20 *hors commerce* copies. Edition: 345 copies (25
on Shidzuoka japan with a suite on china; 320 on
Arches wove, incl. 20 *hors commerce*). Copy no. XIX.

1976:18-145

(36)

(35)

Edouard Vuillard   1868-1940

(37)

Cuisine, recueil de 117 recettes

Henry Jean Laroche

Paris, Arts et Métiers Graphiques (1935)

146p., 3f.; 6 lithographs *hors texte* by Vuillard, of which 4 printed in black and 2 in brown (unsigned); 6 etchings *hors texte* by André Dunoyer de Segonzac printed in black (unsigned); 6 etchings *hors texte* by

André Villeboeuf printed in black (unsigned); page size 13³/₈ × 10¹/₄ inches (340 × 260 mm).

Printer: Auguste Clot, lithographs
         Brunel, Segonzac etchings
         Brun, Villeboeuf etchings
         Dehon & Cie., text

One of 150 copies on Arches. Edition: 170 copies (20 on japan, incl. 10 with extra set of lithographs and etchings; 150 on Arches). Copy no. 34.

1976:18-147

Artist and the Book, 318

(37: VUILLARD)

(37: SEGONZAC)

(38: MARTIN)

Collections

(38)

TABLEAUX DE PARIS

Paris, Éditions Émile-Paul Frères, 1927

3f., vii, [1], 259, [1]p., 3f.; 5 lithographs *hors texte* by P. Bonnard, J. G. Daragnès, L. A. Moreau, M. Utrillo, and M. de Vlaminck printed in black and 1 lithograph *hors texte* by G. Rouault printed in colors; 13 etchings *hors texte* by E. Céria, H. David, A. Dunoyer de Segonzac, P. Falké, T. Foujita, C. Laborde, M. Laurencin, A. Marquet, H. Matisse, J. Oberlé, J. Pascin, K. van Dongen, and H. de Waroquier printed in black and 1 etching *hors texte* by C. Martin printed in color; page size 12³/₄ × 9⁷/₈ inches (325 × 250 mm).

Printer: La Roseraie, etchings
      Duchatel, lithographs
      Coulouma (H. Barthélemy, director), text

One of 200 copies on Rives wove. Edition: 225 copies (25 on imperial japan with a suite on Arches; 200 on Rives wove). There were also several copies on both papers for collaborators. Copy no. 134.

1976:18-92

(40: DE BRAVURA)

(39)

PARIS 1937

[Paris, 1937]

10f., 294p., 3f. incl. 62 etchings by G. Ambroselli, L. R. Antral, M. Asselin, G. Belot, M. Berdon, G. Bofa, P. Bonnard, J. Boullaire, J. L. Boussingault, L. Bruni, C. Camoin, E. Céria, Chériane, E. Corneau, J. G. Daragnès, H. David, A. Derain, G. Desvallières, A. Dignimont, P. Dubreuil, G. L. Dufrenoy, R. Dufy, A. Dunoyer de Segonzac, R. Durey, P. Falké, J. Frélaut, E. O. Friesz, D. E. Galanis, P. E. Gernez, E. Goerg, R. Grillon, M. Gromaire, G. L. Guyot, P. Kayser, M. Kisling, C. Laborde, J. E. Laboureur, M. Laurencin, H. Lebasque, C. Le Breton, P. Le Doux, Léopold-Lèvy, J. M. Le Tournier, A. Lhote, R. Lotiron, B. Mahn, J. Marchand, A. Marquet, H. Matisse, L. A. Moreau, L. Neillot, R. Oudot, J. Puy, J. C. R. Renefer, C. Reymond, M. Savin, C. Serveau, L. Touchagues, K. van Dongen, H. Vergé-Sarrat, M. de Vlaminck, and E. Vuillard printed in black; page size $13^{7}/_{8} \times 10^{3}/_{4}$ inches (350×270 mm).

Printer: Daragnès

Copy no. 149 of an edition of 500 copies.

1976:18-102

(40)

LE BOUQUET DE LA MARIÉE

Gabriel Joseph Gros

Paris, Marcel Sautier, 1945

2f., 70p., 1f. incl. 1 drypoint by D. de Bravura printed in black; 5 lithographs *hors texte* by A. André, R. Demeurisse, H. Le Grix, A. Marchand, and A. Planson printed in black; 2 engravings *hors texte* by P. Dubreuil and R. Haasen printed in black; 11 etchings *hors texte* by M. Asselin, P. E. Clairin, E. Corneau, A. Fraye, E. Goerg, E. Heuzé, M. Laurencin, H. Marre, M. Savin, S. Tourte, and L. Valtat printed in black; 12 drypoints *hors texte* by V. Barbey, C. Berg, D. de Bravura, M. Ciry, J. Crotti, H. David, A. Derain, E. O. Friesz, R. Lotiron, J. Serrière, K. Terechkovitch, and L. Touchagues; page size $8^{7}/_{8} \times 5^{3}/_{4}$ inches (225×145 mm).

Printer: Desjobert, Haasen, and Mourlot, illustrations Chaix, text

Copy no. 184 of an edition of 230 on Lana (the first 30 with a suite in sanguine). There were also 400 copies without illustrations.

1976:18-85

(39: VUILLARD)

(29)

Books containing original prints

BONNARD: Werth, Léon. *Éloge de Bonnard.* [Paris] Bruker [1946]. 10 lithographs by Bonnard. Copy no. 171 of 200.

CÉZANNE: *Cézanne.* Texts by Octave Mirbeau, Théodore Duret, Léon Werth, and Frantz Jourdain. Paris, Bernheim-Jeune, 1914. 1 etching by Cézanne; lithographs after Cézanne by E. Vuillard, P. Bonnard, M. Denis, H. Matisse, and K.-X. Roussel; 1 lithograph by A. Maillol.

CHAGALL: Lassaigne, Jacques. *Chagall.* [Paris] Maeght, 1957. 13 color lithographs by Chagall.

DERAIN: Hilaire, Georges. *Derain.* Genève, Cailler, 1959. No. 8 of 25 deluxe copies with a suite comprising 6 woodcuts, 9 drypoints, and 1 color lithograph by Derain.

DUFY: Berr de Turique, Marcelle. *Raoul Dufy.* Paris, Floury, 1930. 1 etching (frontispiece) by Dufy.
Catalogue complet des éditions Ambroise Vollard. Paris, Le Portique [1930]. 1 etching (frontispiece) by Dufy.
Courthion, Pierre. *Raoul Dufy.* Genève, Cailler, 1951. 4 suites, each of the same 6 etchings and 1 lithograph by Dufy, on 4 different papers.

MANET: Duret, Théodore. *Histoire d'Édouard Manet et de son oeuvre.* Paris, Floury, 1902. 1 etching by Manet.
Duret, Théodore. *Édouard Manet: Sein Leben und seine Kunst.* Berlin, Cassirer, 1910. Trans. by E. Waldmann-Bremen. 2 etchings by Manet and 1 wood-engraving after Manet signed J. B.

MATISSE: Matisse, Henri. *Portraits.* Monte Carlo, Sauret, 1954. 1 lithograph (frontispiece) by Matisse.

PICASSO: Mourlot, Fernand. *Picasso lithographe.* 4 vols. Paris, Sauret 1949-64. 8 lithographs (cover and frontispiece of each volume) by Picasso.

RENOIR: Vollard, Ambroise. *La vie et l'oeuvre de Pierre Auguste Renoir.* Paris, Vollard, 1919.
1 etching (frontispiece) by Renoir present in duplicate.

VUILLARD: Giraudoux, Jean. *Tombeau de Édouard Vuillard.* [Paris] Pour les amis de Vuillard [1944]. 5 etchings by Vuillard.

Duret, Théodore. *Histoire des peintres impressionistes.* Paris, Floury, 1906. 1 wood-engraving by L. Pissarro after C. Pissarro and 1 by Prunaire after Berthe Morisot, etchings by C. Pissarro, by Renoir (2), Cézanne, and Guillaumin (in 3 colors), and by P. M. Roy after Sisley.

Portfolios

VLAMINCK: Duhamel, Georges. *Notre pain quotidien*. Paris, 1963. 7 original etchings and drypoints by Vlaminck as well as 13 reproductions, one on portfolio cover, of Vlaminck watercolors, gouaches, and wash drawings.

MAILLOL: *Daphnis et Chloë, bois originaux d'Aristide Maillol*. [Paris, Philippe Gonin, 1937?]. Unnumbered edition of 49 woodcuts printed in black.

Daphnis et Chloë, bois originaux d'Aristide Maillol. [Paris, Philippe Gonin, 1937?]. Unnumbered edition of 49 woodcuts and one sheet with 4 initial letters printed in red.

TOULOUSE-LAUTREC: *Quatorze lithographies originales de Toulouse-Lautrec pour illustrer des chansons*. Paris, A. Richard [n.d.]. Copy no. 83 of 100. 14 lithographic reprints of music sheet covers for Jean Richepin poems set to music by Désiré Dihau.

(10)

Books illustrated with reproductions

BONNARD: Bonnard, Pierre. *Correspondences.* Paris, Tériade [1944].

Terrasse, Claude. *Petit solfège illustré.* Paris, Quantin [1893].

FORAIN: Forain, J. L. *La vie.* Paris, Juven [n.d.].

GAUGUIN: Gauguin, Paul. *Noa Noa, voyage à Tahiti.* Stockholm, Jan Förlag [1947].

Gauguin, Paul. *Onze menus.* Introd. by Robert Rey. Genève, Cramer, 1950. (Copy no. 361 of 450.)

Gauguin, Paul. *Le sourire.* Introd. and notes by L. J. Bouge. Paris, Maisonneuve, 1952.

MAILLOL: Lifar, Serge. *Pensées sur la danse.* Introd. by Paul Valéry. Paris, Bordes [1946].

MARQUET: Cassou, Jean. *Rhapsodie parisienne.* Paris, Charpentier [1950].

MASSON: Tzara, Tristan. *Terre sur terre.* Genève-Paris, Trois Collines [1946].

PASCIN: Pascin, Jules. *Ein Sommer: Skizzenbuch.* Berlin, Cassirer [n.d.].

PICASSO: Aristophanes. *Lysistrata.* Trans. by Gilbert Seldes. New York, Heritage [1962].

Hugnet, Georges. *La chèvre-feuille.* Paris [Le Prat] 1943.

Picasso, Pablo. *40 dessins de Picasso en marge de Buffon.* Paris, Jonquières [1957].

TOUCHAGUES: Salmon, André. *Donat vainqueur.* Paris, Delpeuch, 1928.

Le Mirliton. Ed. by Aristide Bruant. [Paris] 1885-1904. 122 nos. Reproductions, some in color, of illustrations by Caillou, Steinlen, Toulouse-Lautrec and others.

Reference books

Adhémar, Jean, and Françoise Cachin. *Degas, the complete etchings, lithographs, and monotypes.* New York, The Viking Press [1975].

Alexandre, Arsène. *Jean-François Raffaëlli: peintre, graveur et sculpteur.* Paris, Floury, 1909.

Anthologie du livre illustré par les peintres et sculpteurs de l'école de Paris. Introd. by Claude Roger-Marx. Genève, Skira [1946].

Baruch, Paul L., Inc. *Hilaire-Germain-Edgar Degas 1834-1917: 30 drawings & pastels.* Introd. by Walter Mehring. New York, 1948.

Bénézit, Emmanuel. *Dictionnaire critique et documentaire des peintres, sculpteurs, dessinateurs et graveurs* Nouvelle édition. 8v. [Paris] Grund, 1960.

Boston. Museum of Fine Arts. *Jacques Villon: master of graphic art (1875-1963)* [exh. cat.]. Boston [1964].

Breeskin, Adelyn D. *The graphic work of Mary Cassatt.* New York, Bittner, 1948.

Czwiklitzer, Christophe. *290 affiches de Pablo Picasso.* Paris, L'Auteur Art-C.C., 1968.

Duret, Théodore. *Van Gogh.* Paris, Bernheim-Jeune, 1924.

Efross, A., and J. Tugendhold. *Die Kunst Marc Chagalls.* Potsdam, Gustav Kiepenheuer, 1921.

Fels, Florent. *Vincent van Gogh.* Paris, Floury, 1928.

Geiser, Bernhard. *Picasso: peintre-graveur.* 2 v. Berne: Kornfeld et Klipstein, 1955-68.

Goldschmidt, Lucien, Inc. *Jacques Villon: master drawings and watercolors 1908-1956.* [exh. cat.]. [New York], 1964.

Janis, Eugenia Parry. *Degas monotypes.* Cambridge, Fogg Art Museum, Harvard University, 1968.

Kornfeld, Eberhard W. *Verzeichnis der Kupferstiche,*

Radierungen und Holzschnitte von Marc Chagall.
 v. 1. Bern, Kornfeld und Klipstein, 1970.

Kornfeld, E.W., and P. A. Wick. *Catalogue raisonné de l'oeuvre gravé et lithographié de Paul Signac.* Berne, Kornfeld et Klipstein, 1974.

Krefeld. Kaiser Wilhelm Museum. *Miró: das graphische Werk* [exh. cat.]. [Krefeld, Johann Weiler, 1957].

Light, R. M., & Co., and Helene C. Seiferheld Gallery Inc. *Jacques Villon: master printmaker* [exh. cat.]. Introd. by Francis Steegmuller. New York, 1964.

Lioré, Aimée, and Pierre Cailler. *Catalogue de l'oeuvre gravé de Dunoyer de Segonzac.* 8v. Geneva, Cailler, 1958.

Lugt, Frits. *Les marques de collections de dessins & d'estampes.* 1v. and supplement. La Haye, Nijhoff, 1956.

Maritain, Raïssa. *Marc Chagall.* New York, Editions de la Maison Française, 1943.

Mongan, Agnes, and Paul Sachs. *Drawings in the Fogg Museum of Art.* 2v. Cambridge, Harvard University Press, 1946.

Morice, Charles. *Paul Gauguin.* Paris, Floury, 1919.

Mornand, Pierre. *Vingt-deux artistes du livre.* Introd. by J. R. Thomé. Paris, Le Courrier graphique [1948].

Mornand, Pierre, and Thomé, J. R. *Vingt artistes du livre.* Introd. by Raymond Cogniat. Paris, Le Courrier graphique [1950].

Mourlot, Fernand. *Braque lithographe.* [Monte-Carlo] Sauret [1963].

National Collection of Fine Arts. Smithsonian Institution. *Prints from the Mourlot Press* [exh. cat.]. Introd. by Jean Adhémar. [Washington, D.C., 1964].

New York. The Museum of Modern Art. *Toulouse-Lautrec: paintings, drawings, posters and lithographs.* New York, 1956.

Penrose, Ronald. *The sculpture of Picasso.* New York, The Museum of Modern Art [1967].

Pissarro, Camille. *Camille Pissarro: Letters to his son Lucien.* Ed. by John Rewald. New York, Pantheon Books [1943].

Rouart, Denis. *Degas dessins.* Paris, Braun [1948].

Rouart, Denis. *E. Degas monotypes.* Paris, Quatre Chemins [1948].

Salomon, Jacques. *Auprès de Vuillard.* Paris, La Palme [1953].

Seailles, Gabriel. *Eugène Carrière: l'homme et l'artiste.* Paris, Pelletan, 1901.

Sotheby & Co. *Catalogue of a collection of fine lithographs and drawings by Henri de Toulouse-Lautrec.* [London] 1966.

Sýkorová, Libuše. *Gauguin woodcuts.* London, Hamlyn [1963].

Venturi, Lionello. *Chagall.* [Geneva ?, Skira, 1956].

Venturi, Lionello. *Marc Chagall.* New York, Pierre Matisse [1945].

Walterskirchen, Katalin von. *Maurice de Vlaminck, Verzeichnis des graphischen Werkes: Holzschnitte, Radierungen, Lithographien.* Bern, Benteli [1974].

Bibliography

Leonard BASKIN

Brook, Stephen. *A bibliography of The Gehenna Press, 1942-1975*. Northampton, Mass., 1976.

King, Dorothy. "Notes on the Gehenna Press," *Printing & Graphic Arts*, VII (June 1959), 33-48.

Emile BERNARD

Bremen. Kunsthalle. *Emile Bernard* [exh. cat. by Henning Bock and J. H. Müller]. [Bremen, 1967].

Göteborg. Konstmuseum. *Emile Bernard* [exh. cat.]. [Göteborg, 1969].

Pierre BONNARD

Laprade, Jacques de. "Gravures, illustrations, dessins de Pierre Bonnard," *Formes et Couleurs*, no. 2 (1944), 50-62.

Rewald, John. *Pierre Bonnard*. New York, The Museum of Modern Art [1948].

Roger-Marx, Claude. *Bonnard lithographe*. Monte Carlo, 1952.

Werth, Leon. "Pierre Bonnard illustrateur." Bibliography by Bernard Thibault. *Le Portique*, no. 7 (1950), 9-20.

Terrasse, Charles. *Bonnard*. Paris, 1927.

Georges BRAQUE

Braque lithographe. Préface de Francis Ponge. Notices et catalogue par Fernand Mourlot. [Monte Carlo, 1963].

Gieure, Maurice. *G. Braque*. Paris [1956].

Hofmann, Werner. *Georges Braque: das graphische Werk*. Stuttgart, [1961].

Limbour, Georges. "La théogonie d'Hésiode et de Georges Braque," *Derrière le miroir*, no. 71-72 (1954-55).

Maeght, Adrien, Galerie, Paris. *Georges Braque: grands livres illustrés* [exh. cat. by Roger Vieillard]. [Paris] 1958.

Paris. Bibliothèque Nationale. *Georges Braque, oeuvre graphique* [exh. cat.]. Paris, 1960.

Ribemont-Dessaignes, G. "G. Braque, illustrateur," *L'Oeil*, no. 47.

Marc CHAGALL

Meyer, Franz. *Marc Chagall: das graphische Werk*. [Stuttgart, 1957].

Paris. Bibliothèque Nationale. *Chagall, l'oeuvre gravé* [exh. cat.]. Paris, 1957.

Paris. Bibliothèque Nationale. *Chagall, l'oeuvre gravé* [exh. cat.]. Paris, 1970.

Jean CHARLOT

Morse, Peter. *Jean Charlot's prints: a catalogue raisonné*. Honolulu, 1976.

Raoul DUFY

Camo, Pierre. "Dans l'atelier de Dufy," *Le Portique*, no. 4 (1946), 5-47.

Cogniat, Raymond. *Raoul Dufy*. [Paris, 1962?].

Courthion, Pierre. *Raoul Dufy*. Geneva, 1951.

Paris. Musée Nationale d'Art Moderne. *Raoul Dufy* [exh. cat. by Bernard Dorival]. Paris, 1953.

Hans ERNI

Cailler, Pierre. *Catalogue raisonné de l'oeuvre lithographié et gravé de Hans Erni*. 2v. Geneva, 1969-71.

Rosner, Charles. *L'oeuvre graphique de Hans Erni*. Geneva [1957].

Roy, Claude. *Hans Erni*. Lausanne, [1964].

Schneeberger, Pierre Francis. *Hans Erni*. Geneva, 1961.

Jean-Louis FORAIN

Guerin, Marcel. *J.-L. Forain, aquafortiste: catalogue raisonné de l'oeuvre gravé.* 2v. Paris, Floury, 1912.
Paris. Bibliothèque Nationale. *J.-L. Forain* [exh. cat.]. Paris [1952].
Reichenbach, Philippe, Galerie, Paris. *Forain: oeuvres de 1875 à 1895* [exh. cat.]. [Paris, 1965].

Aristide MAILLOL

Buffalo. Fine Arts Academy. *Aristide Maillol* [exh. cat.]. Buffalo [1945].
Busch, Günter. *Aristide Maillol als Illustrator.* Neu-Isenberg, [1970].
George, Waldemar. *Aristide Maillol.* Neuchatel [1964].
Guerin, Marcel. *Catalogue raisonné de l'oeuvre gravé et lithographié de Aristide Maillol.* 2v. Geneva, 1965.
Hentzen, Alfred. "Buch-Illustrationen von Aristide Maillol," *Philobiblon,* v. 10, no. 7 (1938), 336-350.
Kessler, Harry. "Warum Maillol Vergils Eklogen illustriert hat," *Der Querschnitt* (Nov. 1928).
Rewald, John. "Maillol illustrateur," *Le Portique,* no. 1 (1945), 26-28.
Rewald, John. *The woodcuts of Aristide Maillol.* New York, 1943.

Albert MARQUET

Copenhagen. Statens Museum for Kunst. *Albert Marquet* [exh. cat.]. [Copenhagen] 1950.
Marquet, Marcelle. *Marquet: vie et portrait.* Lausanne [1953].
Martin-Méry, Gilberte. *Albert Marquet* [exh. cat.]. Paris, 1975.

Henri MATISSE

Barr, Alfred H., Jr. *Matisse, his art and his public.* Appendix G: "Illustrations by Matisse," by William S. Lieberman. New York, 1951 (reprinted 1966).
Cramer, Gerald, Galerie, Geneva. *Le livre illustré par Henri Matisse* [exh. cat.]. Geneva [1959].
Johnson-International Galleries, Chicago. *Master of graphic art, Henri Matisse: 1869-1954* [exh. cat.]. Chicago, 1972.
Lieberman, William S. *Matisse, 50 years of his graphic art.* New York, 1956.
Paris. Bibliothèque Nationale. *Matisse, l'oeuvre gravé.* [exh. cat.]. Paris, 1970.

(31)

Jules PASCIN

Freudenheim, Tom L. *Pascin* [exh. cat.]. [Los Angeles, 1966].
Warnod, André. *Pascin.* Monte-Carlo [1954].
Werner, Alfred. *Pascin.* New York, 1962.
Voss, Hans. *Julius Pincas dit Pascin: Versuch einer Analyse und eines Katalogs seines druckgraphischen Werkes.* [Frankfurt a. M.] 1956.

Pablo PICASSO

Barr, Alfred H., Jr. *Picasso: fifty years of his art.* New York [1946].

Bloch, Georges. *Pablo Picasso: Catalogue de l'oeuvre gravé et lithographié*. Vols. 1-3. Bern [1968-   ].

Geiser, Bernhard. *Picasso, peintre-graveur, catalogue illustré de l'oeuvre gravé et lithographié, 1899-1931*. 2v. Bern, 1933-68.

Guild du Livre. *L'oeuvre gravé de Picasso*. Lausanne [1955].

Guild du Livre. *L'oeuvre gravé de Picasso*. Lausanne [1966].

Horodisch, Abraham. *Pablo Picasso als Buchkünstler*. Frankfurt a. M., 1957. (Expanded trans. by I. Grafe, *Picasso as a book artist*, London & Cleveland [1962].)

Matarasso, H. *Bibliographie des livres illustrés par Pablo Picasso, oeuvres graphiques 1905-1956*. Nice, 1956.

Mourlot, Fernand. *Picasso lithographe*. 4v. Monte-Carlo [1949-56].

Paris. Bibliothèque Nationale. *Picasso, l'oeuvre gravé* [exh. cat.]. Paris, 1955.

Pouterman, J. E. "Books illustrated by Pablo Picasso: together with a handlist," *Signature,* no. 14 (May 1950), 10-21.

Scheidegger, Alfred. *Pablo Picasso: Druckgraphik*. [Bern, 1972].

Odilon REDON

Bacou, Roseline. *Odilon Redon*. 2v. Geneva, 1956.

Mellerio, André. *Odilon Redon: oeuvre graphique complet*. The Hague [1913]. (Expanded ed. by Alfred Werner, *The graphic works of Odilon Redon*, New York, 1969).

Mellerio, André. *Odilon Redon: peintre, dessinateur, graveur*. Paris, 1923.

Seznec, Jean. *Nouvelles études sur la tentation de Saint Antoine*. London, 1949.

Georges ROUAULT

Agustoni, F. "The graphic work of Georges Rouault," *Print Collector,* (Autumn/Winter 1972).

Courthion, Pierre. *Georges Rouault*. New York [1962].

Klipstein & Kornfeld. *Georges Rouault: Graphik und illustrierte Bücher*. [Bern, 1966].

Milan. Galleria d'Arte Moderno. *Mostra di Georges Rouault*. Milan, 1954.

Soby, James Thrall. *Georges Rouault: paintings and prints*. New York, [1945] (3d ed. 1947).

Wheeler, Monroe. *The prints of Georges Rouault*. New York, [1938].

Wofsy, Alan. *Georges Rouault: the graphic work*. London, 1976.

Andre Dunoyer de SEGONZAC

Guignard, Jacques. *Dunoyer de Segonzac et l'illustration du livre* [exh. cat.]. [Vichy, 1971].

Hugault, Henry. *Dunoyer de Segonzac*. Paris, 1973.

Lioré, Aimée, and Pierre Cailler. *Catalogue de l'oeuvre gravé de Dunoyer de Segonzac*. 8v. Geneva, 1958-70.

Paris. Bibliothèque Nationale. *Dunoyer de Segonzac* [exh. cat.]. Paris, 1958. (English version published by Arts Council of Great Britain as *Dunoyer de Segonzac: watercolours, drawings, engravings,* [London] 1959).

Paris. Bibliothèque Nationale. *Dunoyer de Segonzac, l'oeuvre gravé, dessins, aquarelles* [exh. cat.]. Paris, 1937.

Passeron, Roger. *Les gravures de Dunoyer de Segonzac*. Paris [1970].

Roger-Marx, Claude. *Dunoyer de Segonzac*. Geneva, 1951.

Jacques VILLON

Auberty, Jacqueline, and Charles Perussaux. *Jacques Villon, catalogue de son oeuvre gravé*. Paris, 1950.

Boston. Museum of Fine Arts. *Jacques Villon, master of graphic art* [exh. cat. by Peter A. Wick]. Boston [1964].

International Galleries, Chicago. *Jacques Villon 1875-1963: master of graphic art*. [Chicago, 1967].

Robbins, Daniel, ed. *Jacques Villon* [exh. cat.]. Boston, Godine, 1976.

Paris. Bibliothèque Nationale. *Jacques Villon, l'oeuvre gravé* [exh. cat.]. Paris, 1959.

Maurice de VLAMINCK

Geneva. Musée de l'Athénée. *Maurice de Vlaminck du fauvisme à nos jours* [exh. cat.]. Geneva, 1958.

Johnson-International Galleries, Chicago. *Vlaminck; master of graphic art, a retrospective exhibition of graphic works 1905-1926*. Chicago, 1975.

Walterskirchen, Katalin von. *Maurice de Vlaminck: Verzeichnis des graphischen Werkes*. Bern [1974].

Edouard VUILLARD

Ritchie, Andrew C. *Edouard Vuillard*. New York, 1954.

Roger-Marx, Claude. "Edouard Vuillard illustrateur," *Le Portique,* no. 3 (1946), 47-55.

Roger-Marx, Claude. *L'oeuvre gravé de Vuillard*. Monte Carlo [1948].

Russell, John. *Vuillard*. Greenwich, Conn. [1971].

Salomon, Jacques. *Vuillard*. [Paris, 1968].

GENERAL

Aeschlimann, Erardo. *Bibliografia del libro d'arte italiano, 1940-1952*. Rome [1952].

American Institute of Graphic Arts. *Roger Lacourière, engraver and master printer* [exh. cat.]. New York, 1949.

Arts Council of Great Britain. *An exhibition of French book illustration, 1895-1945*. London [1945].

Beraldi, Henri. *Les graveurs du XIX siècle*. 12v. Paris, 1885-92.

Boston. Museum of Fine Arts; and Harvard College Library. *The artist and the book 1860-1960 in Western*

(14: RAFFAËLLI)

Europe and the United States [exh. cat.]. Boston [1961] (Rev. ed., Boston [1972]).

Brun, Robert. *Le livre français*. Larousse, 1948.

Brussels. Bibliothèque royale de Belgique. *Bibliothèque de Madame Louis Solvay*, v.2: "Livres illustrés et reliures modernes." Cat. ed. by Franz Schauwers. Brussels, 1965.

Buckland-Wright, John. "Roger Lacourière and modern French engraving," *Signature*, n.s. no. 6 (1948), 3-18.

California Palace of the Legion of Honor. *French art of the book* [exh. cat.]. San Francisco, 1949.

Carteret, Léopold. *Le trésor du bibliophile, livres illustrés modernes 1875 à 1945*. 5v. Paris, 1946-48.

Cramer, Gerald, Galerie, Geneva. *Exposition le tir à l'arc*. Geneva, 1960.

Edinburgh. Scottish National Gallery of Modern Art. *The artist and the book in France, 1931-1967, from the collection of W. J. Strachan*. Edinburgh, 1967.

Flower, Desmond. "Some French contributions to the art of the book," *Signature*, n.s. no. 7 (1948).

Formes et Couleurs, no. 5/6 (1948), "Le livre et les arts graphiques" issue.

Garvey, Eleanor M., and Peter A. Wick. *The arts of the French book, 1900-1965: illustrated books of the school of Paris* [exh. cat.]. Dallas, 1967.

Indiana University. Lilly Library. *Beyond illustration: the livre d'artiste in the twentieth century* [exh. cat. by Breon Mitchell]. Bloomington, 1976.

Johnson, Una E. *Ambroise Vollard éditeur*. New York, 1944. (Rev. ed. forthcoming.)

Klipstein & Kornfeld, Bern. *Dokumentations-Bibliothek zur Kunst und Literatur des 20. Jahrhunderts: Illustrierte Bücher* [auction cat. 88]. Bern, 1958.

Klipstein & Kornfeld, Bern. *Les peintres et le livre*. Bern, 1974.

Klipstein & Kornfeld, Bern. *Tériade éditeur — revue Verve* [exh. cat.]. Bern, 1960.

Lejard, André., ed. *The art of the French book*. London [1947].

Limbour, Georges. "Dix ans d'édition, 1946-1956, Maeght éditeur," *Derrière le miroir*, spec. no. (1956).

Maeght, Aimé, Galerie, Paris. *Editions Maeght*. Paris, 1962.

Minneapolis Institute of Arts. *Modern illustrated books from the collection of Louis E. Stern* [exh. cat.]. Minneapolis [1959].

Mornand, Pierre. *Vingt-deux artistes du livre.* Paris, 1948.

Mornand, Pierre, and J. R. Thomé. *Vingt artistes du livre.* Paris [1950].

New York. Museum of Modern Art. *Modern painters and sculptors as illustrators* [exh. cat., Monroe Wheeler, ed.]. New York [1936].

Oxford. Ashmolean Museum. *The artist and the book in France, a personal anthology from the collection of W. J. Strachan.* Oxford, 1963.

Paris. Musée Galliera. *Le livre du bibliophile depuis 1945.* Paris, 1961.

Pia, Pascal. "Livres de peintres," *L'Oeil,* no. 35.

Rauch, Nicolas, S. A., Geneva. *Les peintres et le livre* [cat. 6]. Geneva [1957].

Rauch, Nicolas. "Peintres et sculpteurs français dans l'art du livre moderne," *Formes et Couleurs,* no. 6 (1944).

Skira, Albert. *Anthologie du livre illustré par les peintres et sculpteurs de l'école de Paris.* Geneva [1946].

Skira, Albert. *Vingt ans d'activité.* [Geneva, 1948].

Stahly, François. "Galerie Maeght, Paris: book design and advertising art." *Graphis,* X (1954), 514.

Strachan, W. J. *The artist and the book in France: the 20th century* livre d'artiste. London & New York [1969].

Strachan, W. J. "Modern French engraving for the book," *Studio* (Oct. 1954).

Symons, A. J. A. "An unacknowledged movement in fine printing, the typography of the eighteen-nineties," *The Fleuron,* VII (1930), 83-119.

Tours. Musée des Beaux-Arts. *Le livre illustré contemporaine 1900-1950.* Tours, 1955.

Vicaire, Georges. *Manuel de l'amateur de livres du XIXe siècle.* 8v. Paris, 1894-1920.

Victor-Michel, V. P. *Essai sur le livre de qualité.* Paris, 1948.

Vollard, Ambroise. *Catalogue complet des éditions Ambroise Vollard* [exh. cat.]. Paris [1930].

Vollard, Ambroise. *Souvenirs d'un marchand de tableaux.* Paris, 1937 (reprinted 1959). (English translation by Violet M. Macdonald: *Recollections of a picture-dealer,* London, 1936).

Index

Authors, editors, and translators of numbered entries.

(25)

(25)

(28)